THE WAX ARGUMENT

The Wax Argument

& Other
Thought Experiments

Stephen Payne

HAPPENSTANCE PRESS

BY THE SAME AUTHOR:

The Windmill Proof, Happen*Stance*, 2021

Pattern Beyond Chance, Happen*Stance*, 2015

The Probabilities of Balance, Smiths Knoll (pamphlet), 2010

ACKNOWLEDGEMENTS:

Two of these poems were published in *Raceme*. As ever,
numerous poetry friends and teachers deserve thanks for
their advice, including my Cardiff workshopping group:
Abeer Ameer, David Foster Morgan, Leona Medlin, Sarah
Rowland Jones, Amanda Rackstraw and Amy Wack. Two
friends whose encouragement and critique has been
invaluable are Heidi Beck and Ruth Sharman.

First published in 2022 by Happen*Stance* Press
21 Hatton Green, Glenrothes KY7 4SD
https://happenstancepress.com
ISBN: 978-1-910131-69-5

Printed & bound by Imprint Digital, Exeter
https://digital.imprint.co.uk

Contents

ACHILLES AND THE TORTOISE

—Zeno (c. 450 BCE) *Paradoxes of Motion*

Zeno of Elea described what happened
when a tortoise challenged the young Achilles.
'Race you, Speedy! Give me a little head start,
     you'll never catch me.

By the time you get to the place I start from,
I'll have moved on, gained a few hard-won inches.
When you reach there, I've moved again, and so on.
     Catch me, you'll never.'

Poor Achilles must have been rocking, set back
on his famous, soon-to-be-compromised heels.
Same for me this week, with my email in-box,
     trying to prune it.

Ping!—a new guy pops up each time I bin one.
Then at home when I make a joke about it,
and the laugh she laughs is the one I tried for,
     she takes a slow step

forward, lets the window-light find a colour
on her horn-rimmed glasses, and there behind them
some expression creasing her eyes a moment.
     I couldn't catch it.

THE EDGE OF THE UNIVERSE

—Lucretius (c. 60 bce) *On the Nature of Things*

I come to praise Lucretius, his screenplay and direction,
also his leading man, athlete and research assistant,
who carried a javelin to the outer reaches of space,
running past stars, a white toga in the astral breeze.
He made his way to the very edge of the universe
to administer Lucretius's simple experiment
by throwing his javelin and recording the result.
A hero. Especially as Lucretius will have explained to him
that the main conclusion didn't depend on what happened.
If the javelin keeps flying, there must be space
                                        for it to fly through.
If it collides with a boundary, there must be matter to repel it.
Either way, there's no 'edge'; the universe stretches for ever.
What should our hero do once the experiment's complete?
Retrieve the javelin, search onward for a further border?
Better to leave him earlier, where Lucretius left him,
if not at the edge of the universe, then on the edge of knowledge,
weight on his back foot, his throwing arm cocked,
his free arm extended and raised, pointing at something.

THE INFINITE MONKEY THEOREM

—Émile Borel (1913) *Statistical Mechanics and Irreversibility*

Suppose it types forever and a day:
then almost surely, as the scholars have it,
the monkey will rewrite the works of Shakespeare.

You've got to put aside the pedants' protests:
allow for good supplies of ink and paper,
assume all moving parts remain intact.

And please, don't agonise about the monkey.
It simply signifies a random process
that won't grow old and won't get stuck in ruts.

Concede the point about infinity,
that strikingly unlikely things must happen
because there's always so much going on.

No news to Will. 'Forever and a day'
is his. And check 'outrageous' in the line
'The slings and arrows of outrageous fortune'—

so apposite to our scenario.
Perhaps that phrase came whole as he was working,
a quill between his fingers and his thumb.

He's tapping it against his lower lip
while reading back a line he's just composed
(the feather-tickle of an unstressed ending),

consulting, in some way that can't be figured,
the record of his lived experiences,
expressions he's already heard, or conjured.

THE FLYING MAN

—Ibn Sina (1027) *The Book of Healing*

Born out of thin air, the flying man
is suspended in it, a high-lying man.

He senses nothing, not even his own body
riding thermals, this gravity-defying man.

He is aware only of being aware.
He is a self-verifying man.

He pinches himself. Purely meta-
phorically. Calling-and-replying man.

His mind is the sole witness for the defence
of his existence. Testifying man.

All human beings are this. All these have souls.
He is the middle-term-supplying man.

He persists in thought. Ibn Sina's idea,
now ours as well. Undying man.

THE PRINCE AND THE COBBLER

—John Locke (1694) *An Essay Concerning Human Understanding*

The wooden last at which the cobbler stands,
a hammer and a hobnail in his hands,
is shaped like a man's foot. The boot it wears
awaits essential structural repairs.
A glazing iron, scissors and an awl
lie on the bench; against one whitewashed wall
a fringe of laces hangs down from its hook.

But things are not as simple as they look.
Somehow a prince's soul and consciousness
has found a cobbler's body to possess.
This person surely is a prince, his mind
a slate already chalked-on by the kind
of life no cobbler ever even dreamt.

Yet here in his new skin he must attempt
to mend a boot. He holds the nail in place, up straight,
and lifts his arm to test the hammer's weight.

THE SHIP OF THESEUS

—Plutarch (c. 100 CE) *Parallel Lives*

The great ship that returned Theseus
from Crete to Athens was docked in harbour
   and patched over the years
   with new and stronger timber.

When all components had been replaced,
was it the same ship? This famous question—
   the question Plutarch posed—
   comes to me as I listen

to the guide in Bath Assembly Rooms
giving her spiel on the Baedeker blitz,
   incendiary bombs
   and the requisite rebuilds.

Disappointment makes me answer no—
the material is material.
   In the Octagon, though,
   design strikes me as vital

in the face of Gainsborough's portrait
of William Wade, the Bath Adonis,
   the ladies' favourite
   Master of Ceremonies.

He stands tall in red coat and leggings,
a lavish corsage in his button hole,
   eying the proceedings,
   as if once more on patrol.

Now I want the answer to be yes—
for John Wood II, the architect on site,
 who envisioned the place
 like this, striped by window-light.

THE ALLEGORY OF THE CAVE

—Plato (c. 375 BCE) *The Republic Book VII*

Chained in a cave, you only ever saw
  a show of fire-cast shadows on the wall.
You'd no idea what any shape was for
  or what it meant. You knew nothing at all
about how false your circumstance, how bleak,
  nothing about the guards, the puppeteers,
  disposing sculptured objects on the shelves
behind your back. Whenever they would speak,
  their voices echoed round and, to your ears,
    were spoken by the silhouettes themselves.

Released at last, you struggle to forget
  the murk. The blessings of the sunlit days
are mixed: your eyes burn with the dazzle, yet
  to make the most of liberty you gaze
at everything. And next you have to do
  the maths, especially the geometry.
    The night sky is your workbook. Once you prove
the full moon is a circle, you will view
  a gibbous moon, misformed though it may be,
    as beautiful and true at one remove.

THE RING OF GYGES AND THE INVISIBLE MAN

—Plato (c. 375 BCE) *The Ring of Gyges, The Republic Book II*
—H.G. Wells (1897) *The Invisible Man*

When the shire shook   the shepherd Gyges
was feeding his flock.   He found a crack
and deep in its dark   a giant's tomb
and a gold ring   on the giant's finger.
Gyges wore it   to the gathering of shepherds.
He twisted it inward   and turned invisible,
head to toe   tunic and hose.
So he volunteered   as envoy to court
where straightaway   he slept with the queen
then killed the king.   Because he could.

Fast forward   to the fin de siècle.

Griffin invented   a way to fine-tune
the refractive index   of living things.
To be invisible   he had to endure
its insults and injuries   its introspections.
The need to be naked   in nithering weather,
flight and fight   with frozen extremities,
a sweep of snow   signposting his manhood.
Or coated and capped   for commerce and discourse,
having to hide   the absence within.
The blank terror   of the bathroom mirror.

THE BALLAD OF THE RESCUE

—Philippa Foot (2002) *Moral Dilemmas: And Other
    Topics in Moral Philosophy*

She cruised the seafront in a jeep,
looking for people to save.
Anyone left was bound to drown
in the coming tidal wave.

She spotted a single man and thought
He'll do—until she saw,
a huddled company of five
farther along the shore.

Her 4x4 could save four more
(with the smallest in the boot),
except that the loner was lying prone
across the only route.

Unless she crushed him under her wheels
she'd never reach the five,
and so she reckoned a second time
and helped the one survive.

The ghosts of the five she left to die
haunt her both night and day,
gnashing and wailing that she was conned
by the one who got away.

There's more to moral calculus
than counting out the dead.

> *With a heigh ho and what can you do—
> it's best to stay in bed, my loves,
> it's best to stay in bed.*

BURIDAN'S ASS

—named after Jean Buridan (c.1295–c.1358)

Listen to the poor beast bray,
exactly equally hungry and thirsty,
and standing there, exactly half way
between the water and the hay,
dying of doubt. A travesty

of rational choice. Unless those ears
have heard something? Perhaps it's lost
in thought only because it fears
the road not taken disappears.
It's in the yellow wood with Frost.

Now our beast doesn't seem so crass
to wait a while, to carefully weigh
the unbearable lightness of being an ass.
It tail-flicks flies from its clarty arse
and lifts its heavy head to bray.

THE CHINESE ROOM

(To the tune of Frank Loesser's 'On a Slow Boat to China')
—John Searle (1980) *Minds, Brains and Programs*

Room full of manuals
with a man sitting waiting,
all by himself alone.
Some Chinese writing
slides in under the door.
To him it's just squiggles
but that's what the instructions are for.

> By correlation
> between data and question
> an answer can be inferred.
> He posts it back to make
> Chinese conversation
> though he can't speak a word.

It's no fun working
as a programmed computer,
stepping through lines of code.
Processing symbols
that don't make any sense.
Hanging on hoping
nobody will spot the pretence.

> Send the designer
> on a slow boat to China
> all by himself, alone.
> Give him a robot as an
> intimate partner,
> baring its heart of stone.

TWIN EARTH

—Hilary Putnam (1973) *Meaning and Reference*

It's a replica of our planet,
and every earthling has a double on it.
But what our twins call 'water',
'ice', 'snow', 'rain', et cetera,
is XYZ—a substance we've not met
which supports life and is clear and wet.

And we're talking ages ago—
no chemical knowledge of XYZ or H_2O—
so neural codes that are every bit the same
refer to different things (that share a name).
Therefore, as Hilary Putnam said,
Meanings just aint in the head.

You might wonder, does it matter
that the brain itself is mostly water?
You might be unsure what's at stake.
Is all this thinking ... just for thinking's sake?
You might not care
what meanings are, let alone where.
But isn't it what keeps you awake at night—
a world that's almost this one, but not quite?

A MOTHER LEARNS TO LOVE HER DAUGHTER-IN-LAW

—Iris Murdoch (1964) *The Idea of Perfection*

M's attitudes and judgments slowly thawed,
then turned right round while her son and his wife D
were living abroad.
Where D had once seemed coarse
M now found her disarmingly plain-spoken,
and natural where she had seemed curt, or worse.

All M had needed, she came to realise,
was the occasion and the mental space
to reappraise
her memories of D—
those gestures and responses, jokes and moans—
to acknowledge and resolve their ambiguity.

Outwardly, nothing was transformed at all.
M's correspondence with D could hardly become
more thoughtful,
more plainly affectionate.
As before, her letters closely mirrored
M's courtesy whenever they had met.

The words and expressions M chose,
her characteristic style and register—
no change to those.
One secret difference:
the pleasure M took in voicing her own phrases
as she tried them out for rhythm and for sense.

M found new meaning also in the same
old mechanics—nudging her favourite ballpoint pen
to sign her name
with offers of love and hope
before folding the crisp, translucent pages
into the pale blue airmail envelope.

THE WAX ARGUMENT

—René Descartes (1641) *Meditations on First
  Philosophy, Second Meditation*

Cool on my palm is one *petite
boule.* It's pale yellow, smooth, discrete.
I hold it underneath my nose
and sniff—is that a hint of rose?
I touch it with my tongue. It's sweet,
still honeyed from the hive, a treat
to contemplate, if not to eat.
So many ways my body knows
this piece of wax.
As I approach the fireside heat,
my sense impressions all retreat
or shift. Even its shape now goes—
and yet its essence, I suppose,
persists. A concept, a conceit,
this piece of wax.

BERTRAND RUSSELL'S TEAPOT

—Bertrand Russell (1952) *Is there a God?*

How casually he flung it into space
merely by mention.
A china teapot orbiting the sun

between the Earth and Mars,
too small and far away
to see with any telescope,

member of a tea set
in the set of all sets
that might not exist

but we know it's there, or at least here,
speeding through the heliosphere
of the mind

with a year of circa 20 earth-months,
a velocity of 60,000 mph
and an attitude I can't work out—

perhaps gyrating,
a mad-hattery meteoroid;
perhaps purposefully following

the nose of its spout,
a satellite on a mission
to be thought about.

IN A PARISIAN CAFÉ

— Jean-Paul Sartre (1943) *Being and Nothingness*

The café-goers disappear in smoky air:
leaving Pierre, who isn't here.

THE MISSING SHADE OF BLUE

—David Hume (1739) *A Treatise of Human Nature*

There's one particular shade of blue
you've never seen. But when you view
the other shades, ordered by hue
    from deep to light,
its absence will be clear to you—
    if Hume was right.

What's more, he claimed you could restore
the missing shade of blue by pure
thought. Maybe this is what thought's for,
    to make or find
a colour you've not seen before
    inside your mind.

BEING A BAT

—Thomas Nagel (1974) *What is it Like to be a Bat?*

If you're a bat, how does it feel
to blow your nose and send a high-pitched squeal
into the cool air of the night
ahead of all those sudden leaps of flight?
Is it a pain, finding your way
by processing a messy overlay
of pressure waves, parsing it out?
Does a sound map leave any space for doubt?
Do some bats wonder what life's all about?

How is it possible to doze
while hanging from a rock face by your toes?
Do eyeballs by the end of day
weigh more, as if a headache's on the way?
Do vampire bats feel blessed or cursed
to wake up nightly with a raging thirst?
And when those teeth get bared above
a sleeping man, what are bats thinking of?
That longing—is it anything like love?

MARY THE COLOUR SCIENTIST

—Frank Jackson (1982) *Epiphenomenal Qualia*

Mary's life was a kind of sacrifice
for science. Her milieu was devoid of colour,
literally. Her meals of milk and rice
were posted through the darkened door of her cellar
with its monochrome computer on which—get this—
she spent her days researching colour vision!
A genius, she mapped the processes
in full, acquired all the physical information

and primed with this, she stepped outside. Then what?
Did she learn something beyond the physical?
(Cf. the qualia of love, for one
who dressed in black and white and like a nun
learned how to kiss from Bogart and Bacall—
Dark Passage; The Big Sleep; To Have and Have Not.)

Notes

All poems included are based on philosophical thought experiments—fictional vignettes that challenge or boost our intuitions about philosophical questions. Some of these philosophical source texts are more often called 'thought experiment' than others and some are more often collected in popular lists, but all are well known and widely discussed—it's easy to find more information about them if required. Poem titles are mainly drawn from the conventional name for the experiment/argument. Epigraphs cite the author and title of the book, essay or scientific article where the idea was first published. 'One particular shade of blue' is David Hume's own phrase.

Most of the poems observe traditional forms. Perhaps the least familiar is the *ci* (pronounced 'tsur'), a Chinese form in which new words are offered for an old tune. The *ci* was, believe it or not, most popular during the Song dynasty.

Some of the poems borrow stanza forms from particular poems: for example, Donne's 'The Flea', Keats' 'Ode on a Grecian Urn', Pound's 'In a Station of the Metro', Frost's 'The Road Not Taken' and Wilbur's 'The Beautiful Changes'.

Filling
and poverty
the gap

Will McMahon • Tim Marsh

CPAG • 94 WHITE LION STREET • LONDON N1 9PF

CPAG promotes action for the relief, directly or indirectly, of poverty among children and families with children. We work to ensure that those on low incomes get their full entitlements to welfare benefits. In our campaigning and information work we seek to improve benefits and policies for low-income families in order to eradicate the injustice of poverty. If you are not already supporting us, please consider making a donation, or ask for details of our membership schemes and publications.

Poverty Publication 100

Published by CPAG
94 White Lion Street, London N1 9PF

© CPAG 1999

ISBN 1 901698 25 4

Photo on front cover © Joanne O'Brien/Format
Cover design and typesetting by Taylor McKenzie 020 7613 3130
Printed by Progressive Printing UK Ltd 01702 524028

CONTENTS

ACKNOWLEDGEMENTS

CPAG would like to acknowledge the support and advice of Joe Harvey of the Health Education Trust and thank him for his time and effort in reviewing this book.

Introduction

'I am a child of a single mother and I enjoy the school meals and my mummy can't afford to make butties.' John Hadden, aged five, from Wrexham in Clwyd.

'I go to work to keep my mind busy, but I am thousands of pounds overdrawn as I have to pay for childcare. I think it would be a help to get free school meals. My friend has a partner with three kids too, still they are struggling!' Mrs Chard from London.

'I am on income support and my two children rely on free school meals. However, West Sussex has recently decided to scrap our hot school meals. It is now even more obvious who the free school meal children are as better-off parents are resorting to packed lunches. I have, therefore, forfeited my entitlement to school meals and provide my own packed lunch for my children. This is very hard financially and makes a very significant difference to our budget, but I do not feel that it is fair to put my children through this stigmatisation.' Gill from West Sussex.

One in three school children in the UK – around 2.8 million – currently live in poverty.[1] Yet only about 1.8 million children are entitled to a free school meal. Of these, around 300,000 (20 per cent), for a variety of reasons, do not take up their entitlement.[2] There are, therefore, around a million children living in poverty who do not get a free school meal.

Every child, irrespective of income level, should have access to a satisfying and nutritious meal during the school day. As this publication shows, many children are missing out on this meal and many low-income families face financial difficulties to ensure their children eat a proper lunch. CPAG believes it is unacceptable to put children and families in this position and urges the Government to remedy the situation.

In March 1999, in response to both research showing that so many children were missing out on a vital meal and to the Acheson report on health inequalities,[3] CPAG launched a new campaign, 'Free School Meals for children who need them'. The campaign has three main aims:

- To extend free school meal provision.
- To ensure that children entitled to a free school meal actually get one.
- To support the ongoing campaign for minimum nutritional standards for school meals.

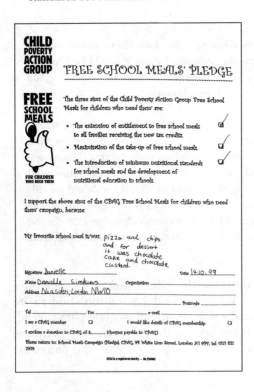

CHILD POVERTY ACTION GROUP

FREE SCHOOL MEALS' PLEDGE

FREE SCHOOL MEALS

The three aims of the Child Poverty Action Group 'Free School Meals for children who need them' are:

- The extension of entitlement to free school meals to all families receiving the new tax credits.
- Maximisation of the take-up of free school meals.
- The introduction of minimum nutritional standards for school meals and the development of nutritional education in schools.

FOR CHILDREN WHO NEED THEM

I support the above aims of the CPAG 'Free School Meals for children who need them' campaign, because:

My favourite school meal is/was: *pizza and chips and for dessert it was chocolate cake and chocolate custard.*

Signature *Danielle*   Date 14.10.99

Name *Danielle Simkins*   Organisation _____

Address *Neasden, London NW10* _____

_____ Postcode _____

Tel _____ Fax _____ e-mail _____

I am a CPAG member ☐   I would like details of CPAG membership ☐

I enclose a donation to CPAG of £____ (cheques payable to 'CPAG')

Please return to: School Meals Campaign (Pledge), CPAG, 94 White Lion Street, London N1 9PF; tel: 0171 837 7979

CPAG is a registered charity – No 294841

By the time schools had closed for the summer that year, hundreds of people, either as individuals or representing organisations, had written to support the campaign. It became clear that throughout the country local activities and initiatives were taking place and that some schools were already placing the provision of a high quality nutritious school meals service, along with food education, at the centre of their concerns. There is clearly no absence of initiative and practical work at a local level.

Many who wrote to CPAG expressed the view that the free school meals service was in need of radical improvement, having been neglected for around twenty years and that urgent action was needed to restore its fortunes. Others felt that the school meals service as a whole had been undermined by the multiple pressures of local authority budget cuts in the 1980s and 1990s and the withdrawal from working families of entitlement to free school meals in the 1988 Social Security Act.

How did the free school meals service reach this point and what should be done to ensure that nutritious, free school meals are provided for all children who need them in the next century? The purpose of this pamphlet, written at a time of tremendous change for the service, is to consider these and other issues and to suggest what might be done to ensure that free school meals are provided for all children who need them.

NOTES

1 *Households Below Average Income*, 1996/97, Corporate Document Services, 1998
2 *Statistics of Education*, DfEE, 1997
3 Sir D Acheson, *An Independent Inquiry into Inequalities in Health*, The Stationery Office, 1998

2 New Government – new policy?

'For nearly 18 years we have seen the quality of school dinners deteriorate and the number of children eating them drop significantly. Last year only 43 per cent of children took meals, compared with 64 per cent in 1979.'
David Blunkett, Secretary of State for Education and Employment, June 1997[1]

The Labour Government has shown real interest in school meal provision. The consultation document, *Ingredients for Success*,[2] issued in late 1998 showed that it was keen to put nutritional standards on the agenda. Following a wide range of responses from interested organisations, the Government announced that all providers of school meals would have to meet mandatory nutritional standards from April 2002.[3]

In the summer of 1998 the Government launched pilot sites for its 'Healthy School Initiative', which aims to ensure that schools use the resources at their disposal to improve the health and wellbeing of children and staff. The pilots, which are the recipients of special funding, will identify what works and what does not work, so that schools can start drawing on best practice to inform their own plans. Food and diet is one of the main concerns of the pilots.[4]

After some lobbying, the Education Sub-committee of the Education and Employment Committee launched 'a brief inquiry' into school meals in the summer of 1999 'to examine the ways in which schools can provide meals which are healthy and nutritious and which children enjoy eating.' At the time of writing, this inquiry is still in progress.

All of this government activity is more than welcome. It is right that high nutritional standards are a central part of school meals policy. One of the central features of CPAG's Free School Meals campaign is nutritional standards as there is still concern that the Government has not addressed how standards will be maintained in the majority of secondary schools that have cash cafeterias offering chips and pizza every day.

Other aspects of school meals provision are equally important. CPAG hopes that the Education Sub-committee inquiry will consider the issue of take-up of free school meals – nutritional guidelines are of little value if a child does not take up the school meal to which s/he is entitled. CPAG also hopes that the Government considers extending provision through working families tax credit, given that the evidence suggests that many low-income working families cannot afford school meals. Once again, good work on nutritional standards will have little impact if, for some children, the cheaper and more filling alternative of the chip shop is the mainstay of lunch provision.

NOTES

1 DfEE Press Release 139/97, 10 June 1997
2 *Ingredients for Success*, DfEE, 1998
3 Department of Health (DoH) Press Release 0462, 27 June 1999
4 DoH Press Release 0219, 2 June 1998

3 History of the school meals service

The ancient educational institutions, monasteries and universities, have long acknowledged the importance of a healthy diet to promote learning. So when free school meals for the poor were first introduced in Manchester in 1879, they provided what had been enjoyed by the elite for many centuries. It was the Education Act of 1870, introducing compulsory elementary education, that brought many poor children into school for the first time. These children had problems concentrating and would fall asleep during classes. It was, therefore, an act of necessity, rather than an act of charity, which lead to the establishment of free school meals.

TRANSFORMATION OF THE SERVICE

As the table overleaf shows, by the end of the 1970s the UK had a comprehensive school meals service, which on the whole had a decent level of free provision for children from poor families, whether working or not. Whilst there was some disquiet over the decline in nutritional standards (the Government had to encourage local authorities to adhere to the recommendations of the Working Party on the Nutritional Aspects of the School Meal[1]) and prices had started to increase, the post-war development of the service created a platform from which nutritional poverty affecting children could be tackled in a systematic way.

However, the election of the Conservative administration in 1979 signalled a wholesale shift in government attitude to the school meals service and free school meal provision. The watchwords of the new Government were choice and parental responsibility. State provision of such a service was viewed as bureaucratic and expensive, and legislation was thought to be required to allow more parental choice in the provision of the midday meal. Private catering companies were regarded as being able to provide parents with a more efficient service at better value. Two Acts of Parliament, which fundamentally altered the post-war school meals service, carried this ethos into law.

1980 EDUCATION ACT

Under the 1980 Education Act the Government introduced a number of changes that began to undermine the breadth of provision and the nutritional content of free school meals. Measures included removing the LEA's statutory duty to provide a midday meal that was 'suitable in all respects as the main meal of the day' as enshrined in the Education Act of 1944. Instead, LEAs were only required to provide meals for children whose parents claimed supplementary benefit or family income supplement (forebears of today's jobseeker's allowance and working families tax credit). LEAs could still provide free school meals on a discretionary basis to children from low-income families. Additionally, the Act abolished both the minimum nutritional standards that controlled the quality of school meals and the fixed price 'national charge'.

1986 SOCIAL SECURITY ACT

The 1986 Social Security Act, which came into operation in 1988, introduced further changes to the system. The most important of these was to withdraw provision of free school meals from families receiving family credit (the re-named family income supplement) and to replace it with a notional amount included in the benefit. In one measure well over half a million children from low-income families lost their entitlement to a free school meal. The 1986 Act also required LEAs providing school meals and free milk to charge for them in all cases, except if parents received income support.

Without statutory nutritional standards, price controls or a mandatory requirement to provide a meal for all children, the national and comprehensive nature of the service was eroded and a system of provision determined mainly by which county a person lived in became the norm. In effect, this has led to wide variation in the type, quantity and quality of both paid for and free school meals provided.

SCHOOL MEALS HISTORY AT A GLANCE

1879 Manchester provides free meals to 'destitute and badly nourished children'.

1889 London school board establishes a School Dinners Association.

1892 Bradford school board allows the use of school cellars to prepare and serve dinners to poor children. School meals are provided by 45 boards.

1893 An inter-departmental committee reports on the poor physique of volunteers during the Boer War. Compulsory education highlights the problem of underfed children. Over 350 voluntary bodies provide meals for underfed children.

1906 The Education Act empowers local education authorities (LEAs) to contribute to the costs incurred by school canteen committees. Boards of education are given powers (but are not compelled) to provide free meals to the poorest children.

1914 The Provision of Meals Act gives the Chancellor of the Exchequer power to make available grants to cover half the cost of meals. However, the First World War leads to a cut in the provision of free school meals from 400,000 in 1914 to 43,000 in 1918.

1920 Over one million children are provided with meals.

1924 Free milk in schools is introduced.

1939 Only half of education authorities (157) now provide a total of 160,000 free school meals.

1940 National school meals policy is introduced. The Government initially provides 70 per cent of the cost of meals, increasing to 95 per cent in the following year. Recommendations for nutritional content, staffing levels and the organisation of the service are established. Price of school meals is fixed at 5d.

1944 The 1944 Education Act requires LEAs to provide a meal to every child in a maintained school who wants one. Around 1.8 million children now receive a school meal.

1947 The full cost of school meals is met by the Government.

1950 Price of school meals is increased to 6d.

1953 Price of school meals is increased to 9d.

1956 Price of school meals is increased to 10d.

1957 Price of school meals is increased to 1s.

1966 Circular 3/66, *The Nutritional Standard of School Dinners*, replaces Circular 1571 (of 1941).

1967 The 100 per cent grant for school meals expenditure is withdrawn and replaced by a system of general rate support.

1967 Price of school meals is increased to 1s 6d.

1969 Price of school meals is increased to 1s 9d.

1970 In England and Wales, 67.9 per cent of children (44 per cent in Scotland) now have a school meal. The Government announces its intention to raise the price of a meal to 2s 10d in two stages.

1971 Price of school meals is 12p.

School milk is withdrawn at age seven except in special circumstances.

1975 Price of school meals is increased to 15p. The report of the Department of Education and Science (DES) working party, *Nutrition in Schools,* is published.

1976 The Government announces its decision to reduce the cost of school meals by £9 million in 1977/78 and £36 million in 1978/79.

1977 Price of school meals is increased to 25p.

On Census day, 61.7 per cent of all school children had a school meal.

1979 White Paper on public expenditure estimates the cost of school meals at £380 million and targets to reduce this to £190 million by lowering the quality of the service through greater use of convenience foods. Price of school meals is increased to 30p.

1980 The new Education Act gives LEAs power to axe the school meals service. There are only two statutory requirements:

- LEAs must ensure that children whose parents receive supplementary benefit or family income supplement receive a free meal.
- Facilities must be provided for pupils who bring their own food.

Charges now range from 35p to 55p per meal. Cafeterias are introduced in secondary schools. The number of children taking school meals drops to 41.7 per cent. Dorset County Council votes to discontinue its school meals service.

1981 CPAG publishes *Badge of Poverty: a new look at the stigma attached to free school meals.* Lincolnshire withdraws school meals.

1982 As more budget cuts are introduced, cash cafeterias are encouraged in secondary schools.

1983 The DES census shows that 51.4 per cent of pupils now have school meals – free school meals account for 15 per cent.

1986 The Local Government Act forces LEAs to put the provision of school meals out to competitive tendering. Buckinghamshire closes its service.

1987 The Social Security Act 1986 comes into force. Children of parents in receipt of income support are still eligible for free school meals; those in receipt of family credit have the price of the meal nominally included in the benefit. As a result, thousands of children lose their entitlement – 49.4 per cent of school children now have school meals. CPAG publishes *One Good Meal A Day: the loss of free school meals.*

1991 The rise of compulsory competitive tendering leads to cuts in school meals services. CPAG publishes *School Meals: fact sheet.*

1992 The further tightening of eligibility rules for income support means that only people working under 16 hours a week are eligible to claim free school meals, compared with 24 hours previously. Eleven per cent of local authorities cease to provide school meals beyond their statutory requirement.

1995 Only 45 per cent of children in England now take school meals.

FREE SCHOOL MEALS AT THE END OF THE 1990s – DELEGATION OF BUDGETS AND 'BEST VALUE'

By the time of the 1997 General Election the school meals service had changed out of all recognition. It was, in reality, no longer a national service that could be an effective instrument for government health policy. One million poor children were (and still are) missing out on a right to a free school meal and at least 300,000 did not receive the meal to which they were entitled.

All of these changes took place against a backdrop of increasing child poverty. In 1979 one child in ten (1.4 million) was living in poverty. By 1997 this figure had tripled to over 4.5 million – one in three children. Precisely at a time when free school meal provision could have been a central feature of an anti-poverty strategy the service was marginalised in terms of education provision and standards left to the discretion of already squeezed local authority budgets.

The importance of free school meals for children on low incomes was most recently emphasised by the Acheson report on health inequalities, published in late 1998. This report, commissioned by the Government, argued:

'There may be a case for extending provision of free school lunches to include children from poor families who are not currently entitled, in order to relieve overall pressure on the family food budget, and improve the nutrition of other family members.'[2]

This point is reinforced by the conclusion drawn by the earlier Department for Education and Employment (DfEE) report, *Eating Well at School*, which suggested that, for many children, the school dinner is the main meal of the day.[3]

The final step in the transformation of the school meals service will come with the delegation of budgets to all secondary schools from April 2000 – a measure that will abolish grant maintained status. All secondary schools will have control over many additional aspects of their own budgets, including the provision of all school meals. It will also be possible for primary and special schools to control their own school meals budget, but it is widely felt that many will choose to stay under the wing of the local education authority.

All schools that decide to opt into the meals service offered by the local authority will have their quality and performance monitored as a part of the Government's new quality assurance initiative, 'Best Value', enshrined in the 1999 Local Government Bill. Best Value, which replaces compulsory competitive tendering introduced by the previous Conservative administration, has four basic principles:

- Consultation with taxpayers, service users and people with an interest in the authority's functions.
- Effective planning processes.
- Performance measurement.
- Continuous improvement in quality and cost.

Best Value offers an opportunity for both parents and children to ensure that local authority catering services are providing a quality school meals service. There is advice in Appendix 2 to help those who want to campaign on the issue.

However, Best Value will not apply to any school that does not want the service provided by the local authority and opts to have a contract with a caterer of its own choice. In such cases, either by choice of outside contractor or through in-house catering, the governing body of these schools will have a fundamental responsibility for the type and quality of the school meals service. It will be for parents, those employed by the school and school children to ensure standards are as high, or higher, as those provided by the local authority.

NOTES

1 N Berger, *The School Meals Service*, Northcote House, 1990, pp50–51
2 Sir D Acheson, *An Independent Inquiry into Inequalities in Health*, The Stationery Office, 1998, p44
3 *Eating Well at School*, DfEE, 1997 p4

4 Free school meals for those who are entitled – tackling low take-up

The Government has clearly stated that it intends to introduce mandatory nutritional standards for all school meals from April 2002. This is a welcome first-term initiative. But it is vital to prioritise new research into why take-up of free school meals is not higher if children from low-income backgrounds are to benefit, and there are signs that the Government may well look at the issue. The whole system of nutritional standards will be undermined if a third of a million of the poorest children do not make it to the dinner queue.

In some areas take-up is much worse than in others. In some London boroughs over one third of school children miss out on a school meal to which they are entitled. Secondary schools in the North East also show high rates of non-take-up – as high as 40 per cent.[1] That so many children who live in poverty are not eating such an essential meal should be of concern; given that one in four children do not get a hot dinner in the evenings,[2] many are missing out on their main hot meal of the day.

Research shows that there are a number of reasons for the non-take-up of free school meals.

STIGMA

A key factor is the stigma that is attached to the provision. Some schools still have separate queues for free meals, other children can be made to wait until paying children have received their lunch. In schools with cash cafeterias 'cashless' children are easy to identify. For some children, simply being identified in such a way is enough to prevent take-up. Unfortunately for others, the stigma of receiving free meals can be made even more traumatic by bullying from other pupils.[3]

The problem of stigma is not new. In 1982, following media coverage on the issue, a 78 year-old pensioner wrote to CPAG:

> 'I still go hot all over when I hear the word 'free dinners'. We had a teacher who at ten minutes to twelve would say "stand up free dinner girls"...I shall never forget the feeling of shame...I would rather have starved.'[4]

In the same year, a single mother wrote to CPAG explaining the problem that she currently faced:

> 'I explained to my eldest son that we could claim free school meals. If you could have seen the look of horror on his face you would understand why I don't claim.'[5]

This view was supported by the last large-scale study of school meals provision, conducted by the Office of Population, Censuses and Surveys in 1979 and published in 1981. Among the random sample of 16,000 families the study found that 20 per cent of parents eligible to claim free school meals did not do so because they were concerned that their children would be picked on. Then, as now, many children did not claim their free dinner for fear of being seen as different.[6]

A generation later, whilst some children go to schools that are taking steps to avoid stigma, other children still have to face being readily identified and, in some cases, teased or bullied as a result of the way free school meals are provided.

These concerns were taken to Parliament by schoolboy James Roberts, aged 14. Speaking at a meeting of the All Party Group on Poverty in the Houses of Parliament on 24 February 1999 at which Angela Eagle, Social Security Minister, was in attendance, James said of the problems faced by young people living in poverty:

> 'Kids whose parents don't have much money are forced to go to the cheap shops and if anyone sees them then they get picked on in the estate and at school. My friend and I have both had these problems. You also get picked on in school if you get a free school dinner ticket; you get called things like poor boy, scavenger and things that are a bit rude and I'm not allowed to repeat. This makes us feel sad and sometimes angry with them and then we get into trouble and get called troublemakers by teachers, which makes it worse.'

DEALING WITH STIGMA

Although it would be almost impossible to make free school meal children invisible in all cases, there are steps that a number of schools currently take that avoid children being readily identifiable.

Some small primary schools allow children to hand in an envelope at the central administrative office. All children are then issued with the same dinner ticket, irrespective of paying status. Other larger schools accept payment in an envelope with the name of the child on it, collected in the classroom at the beginning of the week. In such cases, it is not obvious which envelopes contain notes and which do not.

A growing number of secondary schools with cash cafeterias are introducing electronic school meal cards, issued to all students with

END SHAMEFUL QUEUES FOR FREE SCHOOL MEALS

James' desperate plea to MPs

EXCLUSIVE by OONAGH BLACKMAN

TEENAGER James Roberts last night spoke up for hundreds of thousands of children who go hungry because they're too ashamed to accept free school meals.

James, 14, said: "If your parents don't have much money you get picked on at school because of the way you have to queue up for free school dinners.

"You get called things like poor boy or scavenger. This makes us feel sad. I just want the Government to talk to children like me and listen to us."

James, who lives on a run-down north London estate, poured out his heart to The Mirror days after doing the same to MPs on the All Party Poverty Committee.

Our own investigation revealed that at least 300,000 children are missing out on their only chance of a hot meal each day.

In some schools nearly 40 per cent of pupils avoid their free lunch and snack on crisps and chips because they are bullied and labelled scroungers.

Schools across the country are stigmatising poor pupils by making it obvious they are getting free meals.

SPEECH: James told of stigma

Poverty

Some children are forced to queue separately from paying pupils or wait for them to eat first.

Others are given bright red tickets for free meals, easily singling them out.

Today the Child Poverty Action Group launches a campaign, backed by The Mirror, to stop poor children being excluded from free meals.

The Government's chief medical officer Sir Donald Acheson said last year that free meals should be extended because a lack of nutrition led to health and behavioural problems.

It is estimated that about 2.8 million children live in poverty but only 1.8 million are entitled to a free meal at school.

The shortfall is mainly because children of parents on family tax credit are excluded from free school meals.

CPAG is to urge Chancellor Gordon Brown to use next week's Budget to put a stop to the scandal.

Its chief, Martin Barnes, said: "The Government must take action."

only the electronic cash till and cashier able to recognise a free school meal card. In March 1999 *BBC News Online* reported that Parliament Hill School in the London Borough of Camden had issued all of its pupils and staff with a swipe card, allowing them to pay for school meals using a cashless, electronic payment system. Parents send the school a cheque or cash that is then credited to the card. When the pupils buy food in the canteen the money is automatically deducted. The school introduced the system, in part, to stop bullies taking money from school children. It also wanted to prevent children receiving free school meals from selling their dinner tickets to other pupils. According to the school, the trade in dinner tickets can mean that children most in need of a hot school meal often go without.[7] As of October 1999, the school reported that bullying linked to school dinner money had sharply reduced and the sale of free school meals eliminated.

Aberdeen City Council's education department is currently piloting smart cards. According to the authority:

> 'The card means that no cash changes hands and, therefore, it is impossible for pupils to know which children receive free school dinners. It is hoped that the card will reduce the stigma associated with receiving free school meals and actually increase uptake.'

Pending successful evaluation, the 'Accord Card' will be rolled out across the rest of the city.[8]

There are numerous examples of smart card technology being introduced to improve lunchtimes by shortening queues and reducing bullying. Whilst smart card systems may, at first, require some maths on the part of the student, anecdotal evidence suggests that the regular prices and portions of most school meals services makes identification of a free school meal student much less likely.

OTHER REASONS

Some of the non-take-up is due to children who are absent from school because of sickness or to parents on benefit simply failing to register for the service because they fear stigmatising their own children.[9]

It may be the case that truancy and the increasing number of permanent school exclusions, of which there were over 12,000 by the end of school year in 1998,[10] also account for some of the non-take-up. According to the Children's Society report, *No Lessons Learnt*, 135,000 children were temporarily excluded in 1995-96.[11] The 1997 Education Act extended the maximum period for a fixed-term exclusion from 15 to 45 days. These are issues that require further research, particularly given the fact that when a child is away from school, parents on income support have the additional cost of providing the midday meal.

NOTES

1 *Statistics of Education*, DfEE, 1997
2 *What are Today's Children Eating*, Gardner Merchant School Meals Survey, 1998
3 T Smith and M Noble et al, *Education Divides: poverty and schooling in the 1990s*, CPAG, 1995
4 L Bissett and J Coussins, *Badge of Poverty*, CPAG, 1982
5 *ibid*
6 *ibid*
7 *Cash Card to Beat Dinner Money Bullies*, BBC News OnLine, 25 March 1999 and personal communication 13 October 1999
8 Communication from Sandra Bruce, Aberdeen City Council Community Development Department, 2 July 1999
9 T Smith and M Noble et al *Education Divides: poverty and schooling in the 1990s*, CPAG, 1995
10 *Statistics of Education*, DfEE, 1999
11 *Children, Schools and Crime*, NACRO, 1998

5 Free school meals for all children who need them

There are no precise figures on the number of poor children who do not receive a free school meal. It is possible, however, using reliable statistical sources, to obtain a reasonable idea of the number of children who may be missing out.

There are around 4.6 million children living in poverty in the UK, 2.8 million of whom are aged between 5 and 16 years.[1] It is estimated that around 1.8 million children are eligible for a free school meal. This means that around a million poor children currently go without.

Around 4.5 million paying children do not purchase a school meal.[2] A packed lunch is the main alternative, with some children buying lunch from local shops. According to the 1999 Local Authority Caterers Association survey, 12 per cent of parents said they did not pay for school meals because they were too expensive.[3] This means that half a million children are excluded from school meal provision because of cost. The Gardner Merchant survey shows that of the two million who do pay, 20 per cent (400,000) said that cost was a problem.[4]

Whether school meals provision is organised by national or local government, or managed by individual schools, there will always be a trade off between price and quality. This fact is not at issue. What is at issue is that so many children are excluded completely or partially because their household income is so low that they cannot afford the meal.

The Government itself has recognised the importance of school meals:

'On its own a nutritionally-balanced school lunch cannot compensate for an otherwise poorly balanced diet, but it can make an important contribution to healthy eating and restoring a balanced diet.'[5]

Currently only those children whose parents are in receipt of income support or income-based jobseeker's allowance are entitled to free school meals. None of those receiving working families tax credit (WFTC) or disabled persons tax credit have access. As noted previously, when the precursor of WFTC (family credit) was introduced in 1988 entitlement to free school meals was withdrawn and replaced by a notional amount of money in the benefit. The impact of this change was to penalise the children of parents who managed to find low-paid work. It is this change that goes a long way to explaining why so many school children living in poverty do not have access to a free school meal.

When challenged to address this in the House of Lords, Baroness Hollis of Heigham, speaking for the new Labour Government, argued that:

'Family credit has no provision to allow recipients to receive free school meals. There is a very good reason for that. Family credit itself replaced family income supplement, which did allow for free school meals. However, it was found that the take-up level was low, and 30 per cent of those eligible failed to apply. It was decided that, instead, family credit would include a cash amount to compensate for that situation. In that way everyone obtained equivalent value, and it was paid throughout the year, not just on school days. WFTC inherits this from family credit, and in that sense it has already provided what my noble friend is asking for. Given the much greater generosity of the WFTC over family credit, the grounds for re-instating school meals as a passported benefit as back in the old family supplement days, I suggest, is even less appropriate.'[6]

That family credit contained a satisfactory compensatory amount was also put forward by the Chancellor of the Exchequer, Gordon Brown, in a letter to the Social Security Committee as part of a special report into tax and benefits.[7]

Simply because a minority of those eligible did not apply for the benefit in the late 1970s and early 1980s was not then an argument for withdrawing it from the majority who did apply, and is even less of an argument for excluding such a provision in 2000. Clearly, the fact that so many children of parents in work still live in poverty indicates that an amount set to one side for 52 weeks a year is not sufficient to compensate for the loss of the free school meal. The notional weekly amount of £2.55 included in family credit in 1986 represented 44p a week in real terms, because of the withdrawal of rent and rate rebates as part of the family credit calculation.[8] It is also a dubious proposition that the compensation could provide a packed lunch with the same nutritional value to the child, given the economies of scale enjoyed by school catering. There was, and still is, no guarantee, given the incredibly tight budgets on which many low-income families live, that the money would ever reach the child in question. Additionally, the compensation is an average figure and thus, by definition, inadequate in areas where charges are high.

In itself, the 52 weeks' argument (and it should be remembered that it is 39 weeks' money spread over 52 weeks) put forward by the Government only serves to highlight the loss for children whose parents are on income support of a benefit in the school holidays. How do they fare during these weeks when free school meals are not available?

BETTER OFF ON WORKING FAMILIES TAX CREDIT?

Calculations by CPAG, based on research by the Family Budget Unit, indicate that whilst the WFTC is more generous than family credit it is questionable whether those who move into work can stand the withdrawal of free school meals.[9]

One such example is Julie, a working lone parent with four children from Ealing in West London, who wrote to CPAG in the summer of 1999. After verifying the details of her budget with welfare benefits specialists in CPAG's Citizens' Rights Office her weekly income and expenditure totals were £337 and £360 respectively, leaving her with a shortfall of £23.00 a week.[10]

Income	£	Expenditure	£
Cleaning work	165	Food, toiletries & household	
Family credit	101	cleaning products	65
Child benefit	46	Lunch	28
Housing benefit	25	Childcare	76
		Rent	65
		Council tax	20
		Water charges	7
		Gas	10
		Electricity	8
		Travel	30
		House insurance	8
		Telephone	6
		TV licence	2
		Clothes and shoes	15
		Sundry/emergency repayments	20
TOTALS	**337**		**360**

Julie wanted to know how much better off she would be on the new WFTC. The following shows how her income would be affected:

Income	£
Earnings	165.00
WFTC	150.80
Child benefit	43.20
Housing benefit	8.55
TOTAL	**367.55**

Julie would be £30.55 a week better off on WFTC and have a budget surplus of £7.55 a week. Yet, as the Citizens' Rights Office pointed out in its reply to her, the allowances in her budget for food and clothes were low and there was no allowance for leisure activities. Currently Julie pays £800 a year (£20 a week) for her three school-aged children to have school dinners. It is evident that providing free school meals as part of her WFTC would give her the financial space to breathe and encourage her to stay in work – a core aim of government policy.

The Government appears to acknowledge that receipt of WFTC should not exclude many families with children from receiving other benefits. It has adopted a formula for the passporting of NHS benefits. Families with gross incomes of under £14,300 a year are entitled to health benefits, such as free prescriptions. The formula is designed to ensure that 'tax credit recipients with less than half the average family income will be guaranteed rights to passported benefits.'[11] The formula targets families whose income is below half the average – that is, families who are defined as living in poverty by the most widely accepted current definition.[12] It is expected that one million of the 1.4 million families on tax credits will be covered (around 70 per cent of recipients).

If the Government were to follow its own logic and utilise the formula for NHS benefits for free school meal entitlement, this would cost £287 million for all school children and would ensure that every child living in poverty were eligible. To cover all children whose families receive WFTC would cost £410 million.[13] Although not small sums of money, this commitment would represent a targeted investment in the health of the nation's poorest children.

NOTES

1 *Population Trends*, August 1998, p59
2 *Statistics of Education*, DfEE, 1997
3 Local Authority Catering Association School Meals Survey, 1999
4 *What are Today's Children Eating?*, Gardner Merchant School Meals Survey, 1998, p42, table 3
5 *Ingredients for Success*, DfEE, 1998, p8
6 *Hansard*, 26 April 1999, Tax Credits Bill Debate col.133
7 Second Special Report on Tax and Benefits, Appendix, 22 January 1999
8 *Of Little Benefit*, Social Security Consortium, December 1987
9 *Low Cost But Acceptable*, ed. H Parker, Family Budget Unit, Policy Press, 1998
10 Correspondence between D Thurley of CPAG, and Julie who, because of domestic circumstances, would like to remain anonymous, May 1999
10 House of Lords, *Hansard*, 8 June 1999, col.1309
11 *Households Below Average Income*, 1996/97, Corporate Document Services
12 *Hansard*, Written Answer, PQ11, 11 January 1999

6 Nutrition

'Food is a pleasure to be enjoyed...Food is also important for young people's immediate and future health. Schools can help young people develop good eating habits, both through the food they offer and through the curriculum.' Sir Kenneth Calman, Chief Medical Officer.[1]

A HEALTHY DIET

A healthy diet is essential to both maintain and protect children's health. It is particularly important in the early years. Inadequate nutrition impedes the cognitive development of children in ways that cause lasting damage. The effects of under nutrition are often invisible, but even before they become severe and readily detectable, they have limited a child's ability to understand the world around them.

The 1944 Education Act warned that Britain should not dare risk under-educating its children in the areas of food, nutrition and diet – a warning that seems to have been forgotten. Children from lower socio-economic groups tend to consume more food away from home, eat more processed foods and obtain a greater proportion of the energy in their diet from snacking and snack foods. A study in 1996 showed that 15 per cent of 11-16 year-olds had no breakfast before leaving for school, 36 per cent bought sweets on the way to school and 27 per cent did not have a hot evening meal.[2] The 1997 *Small Fortunes* report found that poor children were eight times less likely to eat fresh fruit.[3]

The 1999 Local Authority Caterers Association survey found that 22 per cent of parents relied on a school meal to provide a balanced diet and that 60 per cent said that the school meal played a vital role in their children's diet.[4]

What food people eat as children also has a great influence on what they eat in adulthood. Dr S Stitt, from University College of St Martin Lancaster, has shown that over-reliance on pre-cooked convenience foods, which tend to be nutritionally inferior, has a huge impact on children's health.[5] This over-reliance, he believes, is due to a lack of food skills among the population (ie, nutrition and cooking skills). Countries such as Britain, New Zealand, Canada and Ireland, where the teaching of food skills has declined in the classroom, have seen the greatest increase in reliance on convenience foods and a measurable decline in their nation's health. Countries such as Iceland, Finland, the Netherlands, Belgium and Spain, where the centrality of food skills has been retained in schools, have a superior quality of diet and better health. It should be noted that a recent report from the British Medical Association specifically recommends that the school curriculum include nutritional and cooking skills, with an emphasis on providing healthy meals on a low income.[6]

Currently children's diets are too high in sugar and fat and too low in fibre, some vitamins and minerals. Children from low-income families have particularly low intakes of folate and vitamins A and C. The Government's report *The Diets of British Schoolchildren*, published in 1989, concluded that young people depend for a significant proportion of their total intake of energy on three foods – chips, cakes and biscuits – at the expense of more nutritious options.[7] The recent Gardner Merchant survey shows that, despite various nutritional initiatives in schools, the most popular meal choices are still pizza and chips.[8] The Acheson report, *An Independent Inquiry into Inequalities in Health*, recommends that schools provide free fruit and restrict the intake of less healthy food.[9]

These dietary deficiencies can affect short-term health, increasing the risk of dental problems due to high quantities of sugar in diets, anaemia from insufficient intake of iron, folic acid or vitamin B12, obesity and general weight gain. In the longer term poor diet may increase the risk of coronary heart disease, strokes, diabetes and problems with bone mass due to insufficient calcium intake. Some

cancers are also believed to relate to a low intake of fresh fruit and vegetables.

COGNITIVE DEVELOPMENT

Short-term nutritional deficiencies, such as missing a meal, can affect a child's ability to concentrate and perform complex tasks. There is some evidence from the United States that improved nutritional content of school meals can result in significant increases in student scores on standardised tests.[10] Measures taken included cutting the amount of refined sugar, eliminating artificial colours and flavours, limiting preservatives and increasing the number of fruits, vegetables and wholegrain foods. The key seems to be that food has to be fresh. Other studies indicate that children given dietary supplements, particularly vitamin C, experience an average overall gain of four points on SAT tests, although there is some debate about these findings.

POVERTY AND FOOD

The amount spent on food by families on low incomes is between £20-25 a week, depending on family size and age.[11] Unfortunately, many of the cheapest foods are generally the least nutritious – fatty, oily foods, often high in salt and sugar. It is far cheaper to fill up on a diet of fatty meat products, biscuits, sweets and white bread than healthier fresh fruit, vegetables and lean meat.

The National Consumer Council report, *Budgeting for Food on Benefits*, shows that healthy food is beyond the budget of many of the poorest households in the country.[12] The Family Budget Unit study, *Low Cost But Acceptable*, also shows how benefit levels fall short of the amount needed to maintain an adequate living standard.[13]

How families deal with this shortfall in income and the impact it has on food was the subject of a study by the Family Policy Studies Centre.[14] The main findings included:

- Unexpected expenses had to be met by cutting back on food.
- Reconciling food quality with cost was difficult for parents.
- The cost of food and money available were the most important factors when deciding what foods to eat.
- Children tended to receive more of their preferred foods, such as chips, beans, burgers and fish fingers, than their affluent counterparts because this avoided waste.

A survey of the nutrition and diet of lone parents found 'the diets of income support claimants were much less likely to be adequate than those not claiming benefits. Households living in the worst deprivation had about half the nutrient intake of parents not in such circumstances.'[15] According to the *National Food Survey 1997*, low-income families eat more calories overall and get more of them from fat and sugar than high-income families. They also eat more salt, perhaps because the food is processed. These differences exclude any food that is eaten outside the home.[16]

FOOD ADVERTISING

Children are subject to enormous commercial and peer pressure to consume foods that are high in fat and sugar. Adverts during TV programmes for children are more likely to be for snacks and sweets

than during general TV programmes. Between 1991 and 1996 the amount of money spent on advertising children's food doubled. At the same time, with a proliferation of cable and satellite facilities, children are viewing more television than ever before. Research shows that a child sees a food advert every five minutes.

One report suggests that the greater the television viewing of a child, the more likely s/he is to have unhealthy, high fat food habits, unhealthy concepts about food and more likely to ask her/his parents to buy foods advertised on television.[17] These branded foods often have lower nutritional values than other foods and are more expensive than own-label alternatives. However, the stigma attached to the consumption of the latter means that parents feel they must buy the more expensive branded food, otherwise their children will not want to eat it. Recent trends in schools, such as the introduction of cafeterias and vending machines, whilst they may raise money for schools by selling branded drinks and foods, have exacerbated this.

A government-commissioned report, *Healthy English Schoolchildren*, went so far as to recommend the introduction of restrictions on advertising to children.[18] Norway and Sweden already forbid advertising to children under 12. Australia and Ireland forbid advertising aimed at the under fives.

SCHOOL FOOD

Money invested in children's nutrition in school saves money in later life. School offers the best opportunity to influence the diets of children, leading to savings in health and social care budgets, both now and later. Research by psychologists suggests that tastes and preferences can be shaped by the environment in which children eat and by introducing them repeatedly to different foods.[19]

School meals make an important contribution to the daily diet of children in the UK. According to the last major government research into school food, they contribute 30-45 per cent of children's daily energy intake, the higher proportion among low-income families.[20] Children receiving free school meals have a poorer diet and are particularly dependent on school meals for their daily intake of vitamin C.

The most recent research in this area was carried out in Northern Ireland, where there has been little change in the nutritional content of school meals over the past ten years.[21] None of the 17 schools surveyed provided meals that met nutritional guidelines. On average, 46 per cent of energy levels in meals came from fat, with saturated fats comprising 16 per cent. This compares with the guideline levels of 35 per cent and 11 per cent respectively. Having said this, school meals still provide a much better nutritional option than packed lunches, because these tend to be nutritionally inadequate with crisps and chocolate as common ingredients, and takeaways consumed as an alternative.

Generally the nutritional value of meals served in primary schools is higher than in secondary schools because the available options in cafeterias in secondary schools allow for poorer nutritional choices by children.

Research at the University of Bangor showed that children could learn to like fresh fruit and vegetables. Children were shown videos, portraying fruit and vegetables in a positive way, and were encouraged to try small quantities. After they had sampled the fruit and vegetables more than a dozen times they would choose them rather than chocolate bars. This change was sustained over many months and even transferred to their homes.[22]

The Edinburgh Community Food Initiative (ECFI), with support from Edinburgh Council, is currently piloting a school fruit shop initiative. This intends to encourage children, particularly those in low-income areas, to develop a habit of eating fruit from an early age.

Schools will be encouraged to set up their own fruit shops, which will be able to buy fruit at cost price. Children who receive free school meals get free vouchers for two pieces of fruit a week and other parents and pupils can buy 10p vouchers, worth one piece of fruit. According to the ECFI:

> 'Vouchers mean pupils can only buy fruit, that they don't have to carry money and that pupils on free school meals aren't stigmatised.'

It is also hoped that the scheme will help remind parents of the educational and lifestyle benefits of healthy eating and help reinforce the healthy eating message the pilot school is already promoting.[23]

Wolsey Primary School in New Addington, South London, has recently received a lot of media coverage of its fruit tuck shop project. This began, three years ago, in one classroom and has now developed throughout the whole school.[24] The school's Head, Peter Winder, argues that getting high-sugar, high-fat snacks and junk foods out of its tuck shop and replacing them with fruit has been central in transforming the eating habits of the children, their behaviour and academic performance. This project has prompted a lot of critical discussion[25] and deserves further attention from all those interested in nutritional standards.

One successful way of promoting nutrition in schools is by introducing School Food Committees or School Nutrition Action Groups (SNAGs). These should involve children, parents, teachers, caterers and have the option to co-opt specialist nutritionists to create school food policies. The Gardner Merchant report shows that in schools where these exist healthy eating is more commonly discussed, children think healthy eating should be encouraged, more pupils consume fresh fruit and parental satisfaction with school food is higher. The report, *Healthy English Schoolchildren*, recommends that all schools be required to establish these groups.

Torquay Boys Grammar School did exactly this in 1997. By involving students, parents, teachers, governors, caterers, the school nurse and the community dietician, the school made healthy eating and nutritional education a central feature of school life. By the end of the school year in 1999 sales of nutritionally balanced meals had risen to 25 per cent of all meals, with 85 per cent of children purchasing school lunches daily. In September 1999 the school gave bonus points for healthy choices at lunchtime, which could be rendered at the Torquay branch of WH Smith. In the first few weeks of the scheme, the sale of healthy options had risen by 65 per cent.[26]

WHAT ARE SNAGS?[27]

School Nutrition Action Groups (SNAGs) are a means of achieving 'bottom-up' change. They aim to:

• promote health in school;
• give children an opportunity to voice their concerns about the provision of healthier, attractively priced, more interesting food;
• establish, monitor and evaluate a consistent food policy with health as the main objective;
• market and promote healthy choices;
• ensure that both the consumers and providers are involved in, and have ownership of, all food provision in the school throughout the day;
• empower children and staff to make improved choices about food.

SNAGs encourage the development of better relations between the school, its community and health professionals in the area of food, nutrition and health. It is a whole school, whole day approach which impacts not just on the school lunch, but also on breakfast and snacks

SNAGs should be made up of:

• senior managers, such as the Head, or Deputy-head; home economics/health education co-ordinators;
• pupils;
• community dietician;
• catering supervisor;
• parents;
• health professionals.

The make up of a SNAG will vary, but for it to be successful the most essential constituent is the involvement of the children.

SNAGs provide benefits to parents and children. For parents they:

• show that children's health is the primary criterion of school meal provision;
• provide increased potential for a consistent approach between school and home;
• give better 'all-day' nutritional support for the child;

For children they:

• provide a sense of ownership of the school food service;
• offer a service more sensitive to their personal and cultural needs;
• enhance the environment;
• provide a consistent message about food in both provision and curriculum.

If you would like to discuss setting up a SNAG in your local school, contact Joe Harvey, Health Education Trust, 18 High Street, Broom, Alcester, Warwickshire B50 4HJ. Tel: 01789 773915.

WHAT IS HEALTHY EATING IN SCHOOLS?[28]

Specifying plenty of fibre-rich starchy foods – bread, pasta, other cereals, potatoes, yams and rice that all provide energy, vitamins, minerals and fibre. About a third of total food intake should come from foods in these groups.

Specifying plenty of fruit and vegetables – fresh, frozen, dried and canned, or as fruit juice. Fruit and vegetables provide vitamins, minerals and fibre. The vitamin C in fruit and vegetables also promotes iron absorption. At least five portions a day are recommended.

Specifying reduced-fat milks and other dairy products – dairy products are a valuable source of calcium, which is important for bone development at all ages, and of other nutrients. Switching to semi-skimmed or skimmed milk and reduced-fat cheeses will help reduce the intake of fats and saturates while still providing plenty of calcium. About a sixth of total food intake should come from foods in this group.

Specifying moderate amounts of protein – fish, lower fat meat dishes and alternative protein sources, such as beans and pulses, provide important nutrients. However, many schools provide unnecessary large amounts of protein-rich foods in relation to other food groups. Foods from this group should make up about a tenth of the total diet.

Restricting fat – especially saturates, the type found in fatty meats, meat products, cheeses, butter and hard margarine. Specifying reduced fat versions of cheese, milk, and spreads and unsaturated oils can help ensure that important nutrients are included in the menu cycle without a high fat intake.

Suggesting the provision of additional choices to foods containing sugar – most young people eat more sugar more often than is recommended for the health of their teeth. It is best to keep sweet foods to mealtimes.

The body's need for salt is small – too much salt can lead to the development of disease.

Foods rich in iron are very important for secondary school children, especially girls. Calcium is also important for all children and food rich in folates is particularly important for girls.

A similar scheme was set up in a secondary school in one of the most deprived areas of Scunthorpe by the community dietician, Jennifer Davies, and the health promotion specialist, Tina May Ward, together with a member of staff and the catering contractors. Healthier eating options are now a regular feature at the school's newly named 'Ridge Diner'. According to Jennifer Davies:

'The aim of the project is to increase the uptake of healthier food options by pupils and staff within a pleasant, health-promoting environment.'

The school has already noticed an increase in the use of school meals by the students.[29]

The work on nutritional standards has been done. The Caroline Walker Trust has published *Nutritional Guidelines for Schools*,[30] based on reports from the Government's nutritional advisory body COMA (Committee on the Medical Aspects of Food and Nutrition Policy), and providing figures for the recommended nutritional content of an average school meal over a one week period. Practical guidelines for providers of school food have also been produced by the Government for England,[31] Scotland,[32] and Northern Ireland.[33]

A government White Paper proposes:

'To specify minimum nutritional standards for inclusion in school meals contracts, which allow schools, LEAs and caterers flexibility to respond to local tastes and to offer choice.'[34]

As a follow up to this, the recent consultation paper, *Ingredients for Success*, examined compulsory standards, the national guidance and how the standards should be introduced.[35]

Healthy English Schoolchildren recommends that, although nutritional standards should be mandatory and enshrined in legislation, a quality standards approach should be adopted, which could lead to a progressive improvement in standards. The standards need to recognise the differences that apply to children of different ages. The report suggests that cash cafeterias should be prohibited in primary schools, as it is inappropriate to expect children of this age to make informed choices. Secondary school children have more scope for choice, and it is important that the differing nutritional needs of boys and girls are addressed. It is suggested that meal times be staggered, with 11-13 year-olds being served first, with a different menu offered to older children. Tuck shops and vending machines should be carefully regulated, so as not to undo any good work achieved by nutritional standards elsewhere.

According to the most recent guidance note prepared by the Department for Education and Employment, minimum nutritional standards, when brought into force, will be the legal responsibility of the school meal provider. If the catering is contracted out then the catering company will have to ensure that the standards are met. If school meals are provided in-house by staff employed by the school itself, they will be the responsibility of the school governors.[36] When considering the issue of school meal provision it should be remembered that school children in 2000 are much more sophisticated than their predecessors in the 1970s. Because of the multi-media revolution of the 1990s, their increasing access to a variety of food choices, and for some adolescents higher disposable income, children are, more than ever, addressed as consumers at every turn. When they enter the school dining hall or cash cafeteria they expect a choice, good service, good quality food and pleasant surroundings. These issues are best addressed by 'whole school' approaches, linking curriculum messages to a creative high quality food service, offering a balanced diet at competitive prices. Additionally, the involvement of pupils in the decision-making process is crucial.

NOTES

1   Introduction to *Eating Well at School: departmental dietary guidance for school food providers*, DfEE, 1997

2   *Teenagers: an in-depth study of consumer attitudes and behavior,* Leatherhead Food Research Association, 1992

3   S Middleton, K Ashworth and I Braithwaite, *Small Fortunes*, Joseph Rowntree, 1997

4   Local Authority Caterers Association School Meals Survey, 1999

5   Dr S Stitt, *The McDonaldisation of Food Education Policy*, Paper to BERA Conference, Lancaster University, 1996

6   *Growing Up in Britain: ensuring a healthy future for our children,* BMA Books, 1999

7   *The Diets of British Schoolchildren,* Department of Health, HMSO, 1989

8   *What Are Today's Children Eating,* Gardner Merchant School Meals Survey, 1998

9   Sir D Acheson, *An Independent Inquiry into Inequalities in Health,* The Stationery Office, 1998

10 Schauss, *Eating for As,* Life Science Press, 1997

11 Office for National Statistics, *Family Spending: a report on the 1996-97 Family Expenditure Survey,* The Stationery Office, 1997

12 National Consumer Council, *Budgeting for Food on Benefits,* NCC, 1994

13 *Low Cost but Acceptable,* ed – H Parker, Family Budget Unit, Policy Press, 1998

14 Dobson, Beardsworth, Keil et al, *Diet, Choice and Poverty,* Family Policy Studies Centre, 1994

15 Dowler and Calvert, *Nutrition and Diet in Lone Parent Families in London,* Family Policy Studies Centre, 1995

16 Ministry of Agriculture Fisheries and Food, *National Food Survey 1997,* The Stationery Office, 1998

17 Signorelli and Lears, *Television and Children's Conceptions of Nutrition: unhealthy messages,* Health Community, 4 April 1992

18 W James and K McColl, *Healthy English Schoolchildren: a new approach to physical activity and food,* Rowett Research Institute, 1997

19 L L Birch, *Clean up Your Plate,* 1987, Learning and Motivation, 18 pp310-317

20 Department of Health, *Diets of British Schoolchildren,* HMSO, 1989

21 Northern Ireland Chest, Heart and Stroke Association, *Investigation into the Nutritional Quality of School Meals in Northern Ireland,* 1995

22 C F Lowe et al, *The Psychological Determinants of Children's Food Preferences,* University of Bangor, 1997

23 *Aims and Objectives of the School Fruit,* Edinburgh Community Food Initiative, 23 September 1999

24 'Fighting the Fizz', *The Guardian,* 8 June 1999

25 'Food for Thought', *Community Practitioner,* August 1999

26 Caterer and Hotelier and *Guide to Healthy and Enjoyable Eating,* Torquay Boys Grammar School, 1999

27 From *School Nutrition Action Groups, A New Policy for Managing Food and Nutrition in Schools* by Joe Harvey and Sandra Passmore, Birmingham Health Education Unit, 1994

28 From the *Balance of Good Health,* based on the Caroline Walker Trust Guidelines

29 Correspondence from Jennifer Davies, Community Dietician, Scunthorpe Community Health Care NHS Trust, 23 February 1999

30 I Sharp, *Nutritional Guidelines for Schools,* Caroline Walker Trust, 1992

31 *Eating Well at School,* parts 1, 2 and 3, DfEE, 1997

32 Scottish Office, Department of Health, *Eating for Health: a diet action plan for Scotland,* HMSO, 1996

33 Health Promotion Agency for Northern Ireland, *Eating for Health: a food and nutritional strategy for Northern Ireland,* 1996

34 *Excellence in Schools,* DfEE, The Stationery Office

35 *Ingredients for Success,* DfEE, 1998

36 Delegation of Funding for School Meals: Guidance Note, DfEE, January 1999, para 11

7 School meals by postcode

PRICE

The abolition of fixed-price charging for school meals in the 1980 Education Act opened the way for variations in pricing policy throughout the UK. A recent random survey, carried out by CPAG, of 12 local authorities in the autumn of 1999 showed the following price differentials.

Given that delegation of budgets will devolve responsibility for school

THE COST OF A SCHOOL MEAL		
Authority	Primary	Secondary
Worcester	0.84	0.84
Devon	1.15	1.23
Sunderland	1.15	1.15
East Sussex	1.19	1.23
City of Cardiff	1.20	1.30
Edinburgh	1.25	1.80
West Midlands	1.30	1.45
Aberdeen	1.35	1.42
Tower Hamlets	1.35	1.45
Wandsworth	1.40	1.70
Norfolk	1.40	1.45
Lancashire	1.50	1.60

meals downwards, it would seem appropriate for the Government to set a framework for schools to work within. Otherwise, the price families will pay under delegated budgets will be decided by each individual school.

For example, under the current county council-governed arrangements, a family living in Devon with one child at primary and one child at secondary school faces an annual cost of around £464.10 for school meals. For any household this is a substantial sum of money. For a family moving onto WFTC this would certainly be a significant financial consideration. However, if the same family lived in Lancashire the charge would be around £604.50 – an additional cost of £140.40.

The consultation paper on delegation of budgets produced by the DfEE for local education authorities simply states that:

'The Government expects schools not to undermine the duty to provide paid meals by charging unreasonably high prices.'[1]

The follow-on guidance note issued by the DfEE in January 1999 states:

'So far as paid meals are concerned, the Government expects schools to charge for these at reasonable levels. Guidance on interpretation of this will be issued in time for instruction of the duty to provide paid lunches on request; the Department will wish to ensure that schools do not evade the forthcoming duty to provide paid lunches on request by setting unrealistically high prices.'[2]

As noted above, around 500,000 children do not get a school meal because it is too expensive and around 400,000 find price a problem. Given that the Government does not indicate what 'high prices' are, it is doubtful whether such advice will provide a safeguard against the exclusion of further numbers of children from paid school meals because they simply cannot afford them. In secondary schools the complexity of combining the pricing structure of the cash cafeteria with mandatory nutritional standards may well result in a wide pricing range between schools.

Of equal concern is that the delegated budget for school meals is not ring-fenced. In effect, the school can spend the school meal budget in whatever way the governors choose. Schools will come under the same pressures that have led many local authorities to cut their school meals budgets. The Leader of West Sussex County Council, Graham Forshaw, in defence of ending the hot school meals provision in the county argued that:

'As more children are entering West Sussex schools it is vital we expand accommodation, provide skilled teachers and ensure all children have the books and equipment they need. To achieve that primary aim we must make the very best use of scarce resources.'[3]

These concerns are reinforced by the recent National Audit Office report on catering in grant maintained schools which, since the 1988 Education Reform Act, have had control of their school meal services.[4] In schools where catering was contracted out the report found:

'...significant price variations across ten schools. For example, the average price of a two-course meal main course with potatoes and another vegetable, a hot or cold sweet, and a drink ranged from £1.40 to £2.20.'

In 11 schools where catering was provided in-house the cost of a school meal ranged between £1.10 and £2.00.
The report further outlines the wide variation in price of the most

	Price range in pence	Variation %	Average price in pence
Pizza	40-70	75	52
Cheese and onion pasty	45-73	62	54
Quiche	40-90	125	60
Chicken and mushroom pie	50-75	50	60
Sausage roll	35-45	29	42
Chipped potatoes	40-65	63	50
Baked beans	18-30	67	23
Cheese sandwich	60-80	33	67
Cola	40-50	25	44
Orange juice	30-45	50	38
Crisps	22-30	36	25

popular items sold and presents the table below as an example. Whilst acknowledging that portion size may account for some of the differences it should be of concern that a portion of quiche in one school may cost more than twice as much as in another.

Some grant maintained schools have sought to break even on school meal provision, others have subsidised provision, and yet others have viewed the school meals service as an income-generating exercise.[5]

Inevitably, such variations in budgeting and pricing leave low-income working families in the most expensive counties, or schools, considerably out of pocket. The question for the Government, which itself has argued that 'schools should...be aware that school meal take-up is extremely price sensitive',[6] is – should a low-income family, or any family for that matter, be financially penalised and the provision of a school meal to a child put into doubt simply because of the area in which they live?

WITHDRAWAL OF HOT MEALS

Where a child lives also affects the type of food that is provided. Since the 1980 Education Act came into force a number of counties have withdrawn the hot meals service that had previously been in place. Although the nutritional value of a hot meal is not necessarily higher than a cold meal, there are many who feel that the provision of a hot meal is important for school children.

It is the case that in the British Isles few people eat cold food as their main meal at home in November. It does seem, therefore, an unusual proposition that such an arrangement would be acceptable for growing school children. It would also be fair to say that many parents have an instinctive preference for hot food for their children on cold winter school days, especially for children who have to travel long distances to and from school.

In a 1999 study of school meal provision in Edinburgh, based on interviews with parents and children, hot meals were preferred:

> 'Hot meals are nicer, 'cos if you get a cold meal it's just like sandwiches and crisps and that doesn't even fill me up.'[7]

Hot food is also seen as comforting, more substantial and a more appealing alternative to a packed lunch provided by the school. Its provision will also offer a choice, which is very important in a

competitive food market place. If parents are to be encouraged to use the school meals service, hot meals need to be made available.

Hot food provision also requires children to sit together and to use and reinforce the dining manners that they have been taught at home. If such everyday values are not being learned at home, schools can be the place where some children acquire these skills and can be socially included.

Despite such concerns, some county councils have already ended hot school meal provision. Most recently, as mentioned previously, West Sussex County Council made a £500,000 cut in school meal provision by withdrawing the hot meals service and replacing it with a sandwich service prepared outside the county. This has provoked a campaign from parents and the trade union UNISON in defence of the hot meals service.

According to the West Sussex Argus, the Symonds family has recently formed a campaign to fight for hot meals in West Sussex schools. They have written to the County Council imploring it to re-introduce the scrapped service, arguing that 'children deserve a hot school meal and workers should keep their jobs.'[8]

The impact of the withdrawal of hot meals on children who receive free school meals should also be acknowledged. Gill, a lone parent of two who lives in West Sussex, contacted CPAG to explain how her family would be hit by the cut. She wrote:

> 'I am on income support and my two children rely on free school meals. However, West Sussex has recently decided to scrap our hot school meals. It is now even more obvious who the free school meal children are, as better-off parents are resorting to a packed lunch. I have, therefore, forfeited my entitlement to school meals and provide my own packed lunch for my children. This is very hard financially and makes a very significant difference to our budget, but I do not feel that it is fair to put my children through this stigmatisation.'

The cost of a packed lunch for Gill's two children is over £6 a week and has to be found from the existing weekly food budget of £30. In effect, the family food budget for breakfast and evening meal has been cut by 20 per cent.[9]

The financial sacrifice made by Gill, and undoubtedly others in West Sussex, is underlined by the 1997 Joseph Rowntree report, *Spending on Children*, which shows that food accounts for by far the largest proportion of average spending on children. Spending on food for children accounts for, on average, 63 per cent of parents' total income support allowance.[10]

Evidently, further investigation into the issue of hot school meal provision is needed. The Government should review the provision of hot school meals and ensure that guidelines are set on this matter as part of the delegation of school budgets in April 2000. The consultation document on nutrition, *Ingredients for Success*, argues that LEAs and schools should decide whether they wish to provide hot food.[11] If there is no real need for hot meals the Government is obliged to explain clearly why not to the growing number of parents who face the withdrawal of the service, and how those children receiving free school meals will not be further stigmatised. If concerns about stigma are not met and it is felt that a hot meal, particularly in the winter months, is necessary, then all children irrespective of which school they attend should have that option.

NOTES

1 The Delegation of Funding for School Meals – a Consultation Paper, DfEE, November 1998
2 Delegation of Funding for School Meals: Guidance Note, DfEE, January 1999, para 25
3 Letter that appeared in various syndicated local newspapers, West Sussex
4 Catering at Grant Maintained Schools in England (NAO, HC 1153 Session 1997/98, 2 December 1998)
5 *ibid*, p23
6 Delegation of Funding for School Meals: Guidance Note, DfEE, January 1999
7 *Please Sir Can I Have Some More: school meals in Edinburgh*, Edinburgh Community Food Initiative, 1999
8 'Hot Food Fight on Families Menu', *The West Sussex Argus*, 6 August 1999
9 Personal correspondence – Gill would prefer to remain anonymous for the purposes of this pamphlet
10 S Middleton, K Ashworth and I Braithwaite, *Spending on Children, Childhood Poverty and Parental Sacrifice*, Joseph Rowntree, 1997
11 *Ingredients for Success*, DfEE, 1998

8 Conclusion – school meals and social exclusion

The main argument for extending free school meals to all school children who are living in poverty is one of social justice.

One of the first steps taken by the Education Sub-committee in its inquiry into school meals was to visit Whitney Park Infant and Junior School. The Headteacher of the infant school, Anne Tanner, put the case clearly:

> 'I work with very young children. I believe they all have tremendous potential to learn, but I also believe that if you are hungry you worry more about being hungry than you do about what is going on in the classroom. Whether it actually impacts on their intellectual ability I could not comment on.'[1]

Whilst rightly making a distinction between intellectual ability and the capacity to use that ability, the point is clearly made. It must be difficult for hungry children to concentrate. This view is supported by Education and Employment Secretary, David Blunkett, who argues:

> '...a balanced diet is crucial to their (school children's) well being. If you are hungry and you have a poor diet it is difficult to concentrate and learn effectively.'[2]

In the most recent academic research from the United States, J Larry Brown suggests:

'Poor children who attend school hungry perform significantly below non-hungry income peers on standardised test scores... (there is) compelling evidence that under-nutrition – even in its 'milder' forms – during any period of childhood can have detrimental effects on the cognitive development of children and their later productivity as adults. In ways not previously known, under-nutrition impacts on the behaviour of children, their school performance and their overall cognitive development.'[3]

This research is important and should be followed up with UK-based studies. Undoubtedly, there will be debate about its precise validity, yet it does not take a rocket scientist to work out what many teachers observe on a daily basis, that better-fed children can concentrate and learn more effectively.

Being hungry at school may perpetuate the social exclusion that the education system itself is trying to overcome. A report by the Centre for Economic Performance noted that economic and social disadvantage are the most important variables in determining attainment in literacy and numeracy. It argues that 'a serious programme to alleviate child poverty might do far more for boosting attainment in literacy and numeracy than any modest interventions into schooling'.[4] It would seem logical then to address such a question at the crossroads of education and nutrition – the school dinner table.

There are other aspects of social exclusion that are worth considering in this context. Some of the children who find it more difficult to concentrate may well become disruptive in the classroom and have an impact on other children's education. On the other hand, the bullying of free school meal children, usually the result of inappropriate service delivery, socially excludes disadvantaged children and, as James Roberts explained, can lead them into trouble. The report *Children, Schools and Crime* by the National Association for the Care and Resettlement of Offenders (NACRO) shows that 70 per cent of children who truant cite being bullied as a factor.[5]

On another tack, *Children, Health and Crime* suggests that providing a minimum standard for school meals will help reduce youth offending. Children suffering from health problems are more likely to get involved in crime, and that the knock-on effect of meeting this health issue early in life is reduced health service bills when children become adults.[6]

There are many ways in which an extended free school meals service could contribute to ameliorating social exclusion. With the political will the extension of free school meals to all children who need them can be achieved. Stigma can also be addressed through spreading best practice in service provision, with the Government and LEAs taking the lead. The steps the Government has already made in regard to nutritional standards are welcome, but questions still need to be answered as to how these will be met in the context of cash cafeterias in secondary schools.

A combination of measures will help the Government achieve its target of eliminating child poverty. If it encourages the development of School Nutrition Action Groups and, after the pilots have been completed, rolls out those parts of the National Healthy Schools Initiative that have proven successful, then it may be possible for schools which have a 'whole school' food approach to become centres of nutritional education in their communities.

NOTES

1   School Meals, Minutes of Evidence, House of Commons Education and Employment Committee (Education Sub-Committee), 6 July 1999, The Stationery Office
2   DfEE Press Release 139/97, 10 June 1997
3   'New Findings about Child Nutrition and Cognitive Development', J Larry Brown, Director of the Center on Hunger, Poverty and Nutrition Policy, Boston Massachusetts in *Fit for School*, New Policy Institute and the Kids' Club Network, March 1999
4   P Robinson, *Literacy, Numeracy and Economic Performance*, Centre for Economic Performance, September 1997
7   *Children, Schools and Crime*, NACRO, 1998
8   *Children, Health and Crime*, NACRO, 1999

APPENDIX I

RECOMMENDATIONS

CPAG welcomes the promising first steps taken by the Government to address the issue of free school meal provision. The mandatory nutritional guidelines are cause for optimism. However, there are additional policies that the Government should consider.

1) Extending eligibility of free school meals to the children of all parents receiving working families tax credit and disabled persons tax credit. As a bare minimum the Government should acknowledge that all those children from working families on or below the poverty line (with an annual income of less than £14,300) should be 'passported' onto free school meals.

2) The Government should lead a campaign to increase the take-up of free school meals by children already in the system. New research is required to reveal the full picture surrounding stigma, ill health, school exclusion and other causal factors contributing to non-take-up.

3) The Government should consider making the reduction of non-take-up a performance indicator for all schools. Finance for free school meals should be given to the school at the start of the academic year, based on entitlement rather than take-up. It should be ringfenced, with any cash not spent because of low take-up used for a school take-up campaign.

4) Once best practice on free school meals provision is identified, a government agency (such as OFSTED) should be charged with ensuring that all schools adhere to procedures that avoid stigmatising free school meal children and to the nutritional standards to be introduced in April 2000.

APPENDIX 2

HOW YOU CAN SUPPORT CPAG'S FREE SCHOOL MEALS CAMPAIGN

CPAG's *Free School Meals for children who need them* campaign aims to:

- extend entitlement of free school meals to all school children living in poverty through eligibility for those whose parents receive working families or disabled persons tax credit;
- maximise the take-up of free school meals;
- introduce minimum nutritional standards for school meals and develop nutritional education in schools.

CPAG believes that the Government is persuadable on all of these issues (indeed it has begun to take steps on nutritional standards) and your actions at a local level can make a difference.

WHAT YOU CAN DO

1) Join the campaign and lobby the Government to extend free school meal provision
- Join CPAG's Free School Meals Network. This will keep you in touch with the campaign and explain how you can help take the campaign forward.
- Fill in the Free School Meals Pledge form and return it to CPAG.
- Order a copy of CPAG's Free School Meals campaign pack – this is free, but a donation of around £2.50 to cover postage and production costs, payable to CPAG, would be welcome.
- Write to your MP about the issue and ask her/him to support the extension of free school meals provision and to sign the Pledge.
- Ask your MP to write to the Minister for School Standards, Jacqui Smith, about CPAG's concerns about the provision of free school meals.

2) Maximising the take-up of free school meals
- CPAG has government statistics on the take-up of free school meals in all counties and authorities in the UK. Once you have these, write to the Chair of your education committee and ask her/him what policies exist for encouraging the take-up of free school meals. Also

request information on how Best Value will impact on the authority's school meals service. Ask what the authority is doing to reduce stigma and bullying.

• Get support from trade unions that represent school meals staff (principally, UNISON and the GMB). Ask if they have any further information on school meals and encourage them to lobby local councillors on take-up.

• Write to your local school and ask what measures are being taken to ensure that free school meal children are not stigmatised by service provision.

3) Nutritional standards
• Write to the Chair of your education committee to ask what – if any – nutritional guidelines are provided for planning school meal menus.

• If your local authority has already adopted the Caroline Walker Trust guidelines, ask if it responded to the Government's *Ingredients for Success* consultation paper and ask for a copy of any response made.

• Contact your local school and ask what nutritional guidelines it will require its contracted school meal provider to follow in April 2000.

• All local health authorities should be actively promoting the 'Healthy Eating Initiatives in Schools'. Ask the health education adviser, who is usually based in the local authority's education department, or someone in your local health promotion unit about any initiatives being taken up.

USE THE DELEGATION OF BUDGETS TO CAMPAIGN ON SCHOOL MEALS

This wholesale change in the way that school meals will be managed offers an opportunity for parents and other campaigners to ask governors key questions about school meals policies.

Write to the Chair of governors and ask what policies are being put in place for nutritional standards, meal pricing and non-stigmatising free school meals provision from April 2000. At best, s/he will have a considered response to some, or all, of these questions but it is possible that you may kick-start a discussion and encourage a better standard at your local school when delegation arrives in April. Ask whether a governor has been appointed in charge of healthy eating and whether establishing a School Nutrition Action Group (SNAG) has been considered.

GET NETWORKING

There are many local organisations and individuals who will share your concern about school meals provision. It is important to try and get them involved. They may already be campaigning on school meals and will welcome some extra help. Some organisations you might like to try are:

- School governors.
- Catering trade unions – UNISON and GMB. You may be able to contact the local union organiser at the local union branch. Nationally, UNISON can be contacted on 020 7388 2366 and GMB on 020 8947 3131. Both unions have given support to CPAG's campaign.
- Teaching unions – the NUT and NUSAWT.
- Health promotion units.
- If your local councillor is a school governor, raise the campaign with her/him and ask for it to put on the agenda of the next governors' meeting. Many councillors have a lot of experience in meetings and may be able to get things moving.

And finally...
Please remember to tell CPAG what you are doing! We always need examples of good and bad school meals practice and campaigning experiences to help develop the campaign across the UK.